My New Pu

My name is

....

Insert here the earliest photo you have of me.
This could be my sales advert, a puppy photo
or a photo of me with my former owner.

My Arrival In The World

The date I was born ....

The day of the week I was born ....

Where I was born ....

Insert a photo of me here.

Monday's child is fair of face,
Tuesday's child is full of grace,
Wednesday's child is full of woe,
Thursday's child has far to go,
Friday's child is loving and giving,
Saturday's child works hard for a living,
And the child that is born on the Sabbath day
Is bonny and blithe, and good and gay.

My Star Sign & Symbols

My Star Sign is ....

My Birth Stone is ....

My Flower is ....

My Chinese Zodiac is ....

Star Signs

Aries ~ 21 March - 19 April
Taurus ~ 20 April - 20 May
Gemini ~ 21 May - 21 June
Cancer ~ 22 June - 22 July
Leo ~ 23 July - 22 August
Virgo ~ 23 August - 22 Sept
Libra ~ 23 Sept - 23 Oct
Scorpio ~ 24 Oct - 21 Nov
Sagittarius ~ 22 Nov - 21 Dec
Capricorn ~ 22 Dec - 19 Jan
Aquarius ~ 20 Jan - 18 Feb
Pisces ~ 19 Feb - 20 March

Birth Stones

Jan - Garnet
Feb - Amethyst
March - Aquamarine
April - Diamond
May - Emerald
June - Alexandrite
July - Ruby
August - Peridot
Sept - Sapphire
Oct - Pink Tourmaline
Nov - Topaz
Dec - Blue Topaz

Flowers

Jan - Carnation
Feb - Violet
March - Narcissus
April - Daisy
May - Lily of the valley
June - Rose
July - Larkspur
August - Gladiolus
Sept - Aster
Oct - Marigold
Nov - Chrysanthemum
Dec - Holly

Chinese Zodiac

Rat - 1996, 2008, 2020
Ox - 1997, 2009, 2021
Tiger - 1998, 2010, 2022
Rabbit - 1999, 2011, 2023
Dragon - 2000, 2012, 2024
Snake - 2001, 2013, 2025
Horse - 2002, 2014, 2026
Goat - 2003, 2015, 2027
Monkey - 2004, 2016, 2028
Rooster - 2005, 2017, 2029
Dog - 2006, 2018, 2030
Pig - 2007, 2019, 2031

How I Got My Name

My full name is ....

My full name was chosen by ....

My nicknames are ....

My nicknames were chosen by ....

Insert a photo here.

My Vital Statistics

Breed: ....

Sex: ....

Colour: ....

Markings: ....

....

Eye colour: ....

Spayed/Neutered: ☐

My Colours & Markings

Try drawing in my markings on the template below. Do I have any distinguishing features you can mark down?

Where I Came From

Stud/breeder/previous owner ....

Address ....

Handover notes ....

....

....

....

Insert a photo here.

Meet My Family

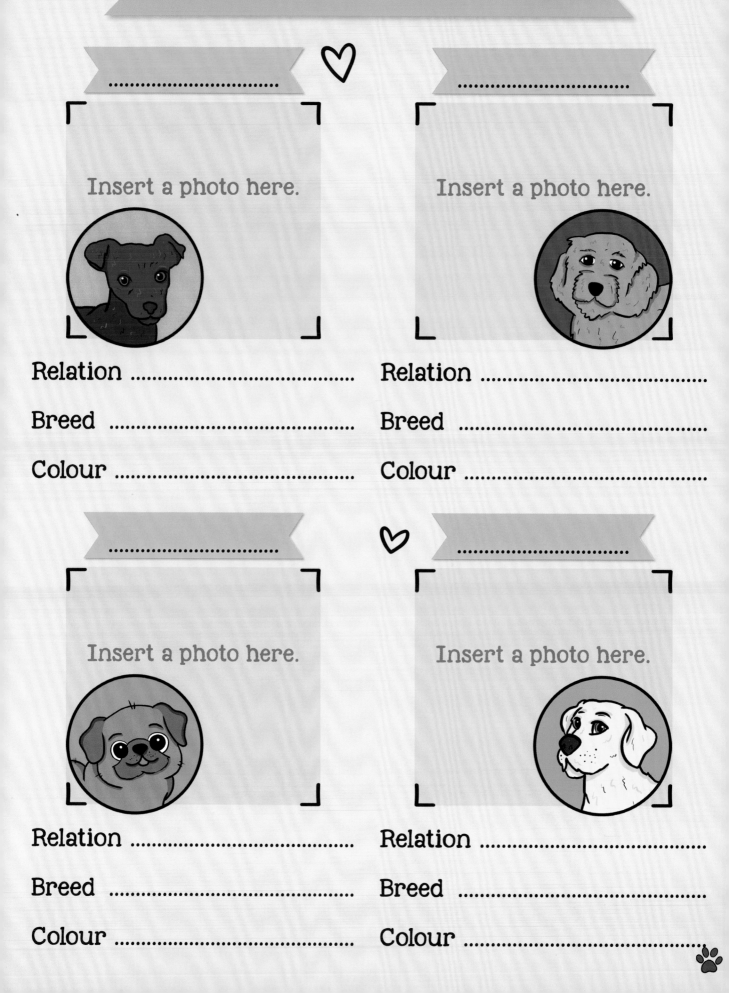

....

Insert a photo here.

Relation ....

Breed ....

Colour ....

....

Insert a photo here.

Relation ....

Breed ....

Colour ....

....

Insert a photo here.

Relation ....

Breed ....

Colour ....

....

Insert a photo here.

Relation ....

Breed ....

Colour ....

Arriving At My New Home

I arrived at my new home on ....

I was wearing ....

My new address is ....

....

Insert a photo of me
arriving at my new home.

Me & My New Human

Insert a photo of me
with my new human.

First Day At My New Home

What did I do? Did I settle well or spend all night crying and keeping everybody awake? Did I meet any new friends?

....

....

....

....

Insert a photo here of our first day together at my new home.

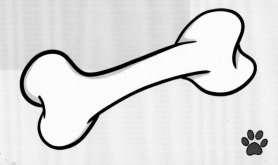

My Paw Print

Place a drawing of my paw print here.
Try painting my paw and then place my paw
on a piece of paper or try drawing around my paw.

Selfie Page

My human & I having fun!

Insert a photo here.

Insert a photo here.

Insert a photo here.

Insert a photo here.

Insert a photo here.

Insert a photo here.

Me Looking Really Cute!

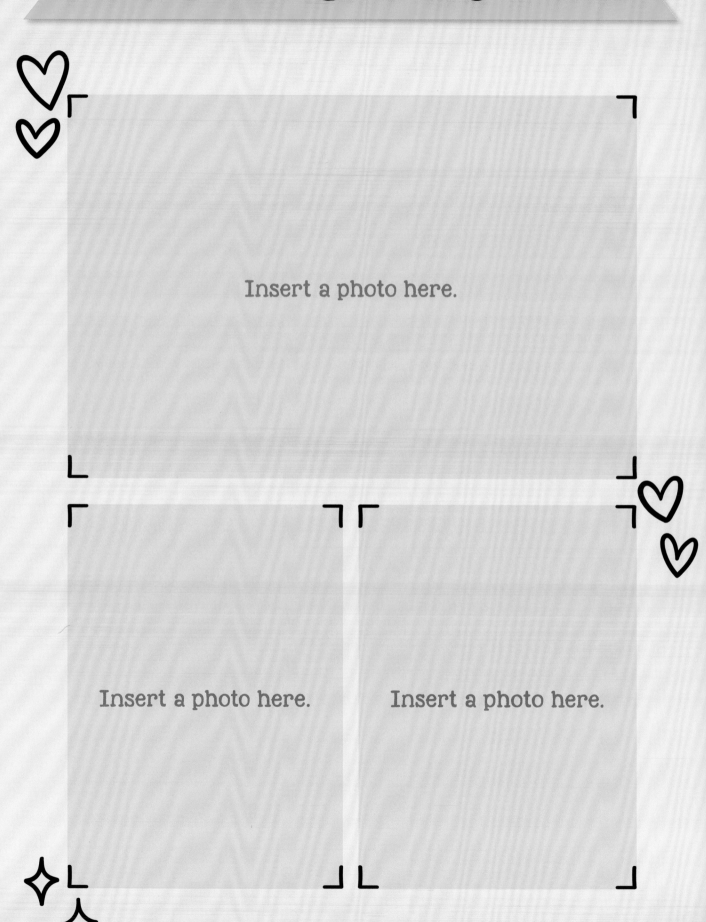

Insert a photo here.

Insert a photo here.

Insert a photo here.

Cute Things I Do

Do I make cute faces when you scratch behind my ears?

My Loveable Quirks

Do I like to carry your dirty socks around in my mouth or do I get the zoomies and charge round and round the garden?

All About Me!

Insert a photo here.

Insert a photo here.

Insert a
photo here.

Insert a
photo here.

Insert a photo here.

Insert a photo here.

First Times

My first walk ....

My first trip into town ....

My first visit to the park ....

My first time being left at home alone ....

....

Insert a photo here of me doing something for the first time.

Insert a photo here of me doing something for the first time.

Insert a photo here of me doing something for the first time.

First Times

My first bath ....

My first haircut ....

The first time I saw snow ....

My first trip to the seaside ....

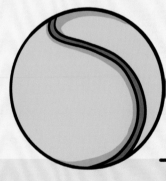

Insert a photo here of me doing something for the first time.

Insert a photo here of me doing something for the first time.

Insert a photo here of me doing something for the first time.

My Friends

Name ....

Breed ....

Colour ....

Things we like to do together

....

....

Insert a photo of
my friend here.

Insert a photo of
my friend here.

Name ....

Breed ....

Colour ....

Things we like to do together

....

....

My Friends

Insert a photo of
my friend here.

Name ....

Breed ....

Colour ....

Things we like to do together

....

....

Name ....

Breed ....

Colour ....

Things we like to do together

....

....

Insert a photo of
my friend here.

Other Special People In My Life

(They could be hairy or human!)

Name ....

....

Insert a photo of my
special friend here.

Insert a photo of my
special friend here.

Name ....

....

Name ....

....

Insert a photo of my
special friend here.

My Honorary Auntie/Uncle

(They could be hairy or human!)

Name ....

Details of special relationship

....

....

....

....

Insert a photo of my honorary auntie/uncle here.

Name ....

Details of special relationship

....

....

....

....

Insert a photo of my honorary auntie/uncle here.

My Wardrobe

Coat size ....

Collar size ....

Harness size ....

Accessories ....

....

....

You might like to list some of the presents you

have bought me here: ....

....

....

....

....

....

....

Puppy & Person Matching Outfits

Insert a photo of me here.

Insert a photo of you here.

A Day In The Life Of Me!

06:00 ....

07:00 ....

08:00 ....

09:00 ....

10:00 ....

11:00 ....

12:00 ....

13:00 ....

14:00 ....

15:00 ....

16:00 ....

17:00 ....

18:00 ....

19:00 ....

My Favourite Treats

I love eating...

Insert a photo of me eating one of my favourite treats.

My Naughty Habits

Do I think its fun to chase the squirrels and pigeons or do I jump all over the furniture even though I know I'm not meant to?
Note them down here:

Exciting Experiences

Have you taken me for my first sleepover or on a mini-break? Have we been on an adventure walk?

....

....

....

....

....

....

Insert a photo here.

Big School

Learning to be a grown up puppy dog

Task	Completed & Date
Learning to walk on a lead	☐ ....
Learning to sit	☐ ....
Learning to lie down	☐ ....
Learning to stay	☐ ....

Insert a photo here of me learning to be a grown up puppy dog.

Finishing School

Some of the fancy pants moves I have learnt:

Things For My Human To Remember

Does my human need to remember to take more than 1 poo bag on our walk, or to always bring a squeaky ball with them and some treats?

Photos Of ME!

Insert a photo here.

Insert a photo here.

Insert a photo here.

Insert a photo here.

Insert a photo here.

Insert a photo here.

My Favourite Toys

I love playing with...

Insert a photo of me playing with
my favourite toy

My First Party

Date ....

Venue ....

Class ....

Result ....

Comments ....

....

....

....

....

Insert a photo here.

Insert a photo here.

Insert a photo here.

Me At A Show Looking Smart

Date ....

Show ....

Class ....

Insert a photo of me
looking smart.

Rosettes & Ribbons

Keep a record of the rosettes and ribbons
we win together here:

Date	Show	Class	Result

My Major Milestones

You may like to note down some of my major milestones and achievements here:

Insert a photo here.

Holidays

Insert a photo here.

Insert a photo here.

Insert a photo here.

Insert a photo here.

Insert a photo here.

Insert a photo here.

Times I Embarrassed My Human

Sometimes I can be a little naughty and my human gets very embarrassed by my behaviour such as when I did a poo on the carpet when visiting friends or when I ran off with someone else's ball and wouldn't give it back:

Things I Find Scary

You might like to list down here some of the things I find scary, such as thunder and fireworks or the puppy eating hoover:

Damage Report

I might look like butter wouldn't melt but I'm quite good at wrecking furniture, digging up the garden and I can't count the number of shoes I have chewn.

You might like to keep a record of my destruction here:

....

....

....

....

....

Insert a photo here of my destruction.

Insert a photo here of my destruction.

Caught On Camera Being Naughty

Insert a photo here.

Insert a photo here.

Insert a photo here.

Insert a photo here.

Bedtime

My favourite sleeping position is

....

....

Insert a photo of me sleeping here.

Hanging Out

Insert a photo here.

Insert a photo here.

Insert a
photo here.

Insert a
photo here.

Insert a photo here.

Insert a photo here.

Insert a photo here.

Birthdays

Insert a photo here.

Insert a photo here.

Insert a photo here.

Insert a photo here.

Insert a photo here.

Insert a photo here.

Christmas

Insert a photo here.

Insert a photo here.

Insert a photo here.

Insert a photo here.

Insert a photo here.

Insert a photo here.

Grown Up Stuff

Insurance details

Name: ....

Policy Number: ....

Contact Details: ....

Microchip Number: ....

Vets Visits

(Accident report)

Name ....

Contact details ....

Visits...

Date	Reason for visit
....	....
....	....
....	....
....	....
....	....
....	....
....	....
....	....
....	....

Vaccination Record

Date	Place	Vaccine
....	....	....
....	....	....
....	....	....
....	....	....
....	....	....
....	....	....
....	....	....
....	....	....
....	....	....
....	....	....
....	....	....
....	....	....

Wormer & Flea Record

Date	Wormer type/brand	Taste
....	....	....
....	....	....
....	....	....
....	....	....
....	....	....
....	....	....
....	....	....
....	....	....

About My Groomer

Name ....

Contact details...

Visits...

Date	Treatments carried out
....	....
....	....
....	....
....	....
....	....
....	....
....	....
....	....

Feeding Notes

When I'm teeny tiny

....
....
....

When I'm a bit bigger

....
....
....

When I'm a grown up dog

....
....
....

Anything else

....
....
....

My Growth & Weight Chart

Date	Height	Weight & condition
....	....	....
....	....	....
....	....	....
....	....	....
....	....	....
....	....	....
....	....	....
....	....	....
....	....	....

Best Friends

Insert a photo of us here.

Notes

....

....

....

....

....

....

....

....

....

....

....

....

....